Jump, Jump, Kangaroo

Story by Joy Cowley
Illustrations by Kathryn Pond

Jump, jump, kangaroo.

2

Jump over the snake.

3

Jump over the frog.

4

Jump over the lizard.

5

Jump over the dog.

Jump, jump, kangaroo.
Jump over the fence...

7

and out
of the zoo.

8